Gerald

Finzi

For St Cecilia op 30

Ceremonial Ode
for tenor solo, chorus & orchestra
Words by Edmund Blunden

Organ reduction by
Robert Gower

BOOSEY & HAWKES

Boosey & Hawkes Music Publishers Ltd
www.boosey.com

The Finzi Trust exists to support the promotion of the music of Gerald Finzi.
For further information visit www.geraldfinzi.org or www.boosey.com

Published by Boosey & Hawkes Music Publishers Ltd
Aldwych House
71–91 Aldwych
London
WC2B 4HN

www.boosey.com

AN IMAGEM COMPANY

ISMN 979-0-060-13040-3
ISBN 978-1-78454-121-7

This impression 2015

Printed by Halstan:
Halstan UK, 2–10 Plantation Road, Amersham, Bucks, HP6 6HJ. United Kingdom
Halstan DE, Weißliliengasse 4, 55116 Mainz. Germany

Music origination by Top Score Music

PERFORMANCE NOTES

This work is scored for an orchestra of 3 flutes (3rd doubling piccolo), 2 oboes, cor anglais, 2 clarinets, bass clarinet, 2 bassoons, contrabassoon, 4 horns, 3 trumpets, 3 trombones, tuba, timpani, percussion (xylophone, triangle, tambourine, side drum, bass drum, cymbals, suspended cymbal, tam-tam), 2 harps (2nd *ad lib*) and strings.

This organ reduction is intended for use instead of orchestra. Detailed registration indications have not been applied. Instead, manuals are indicated:

I – Great
II – Swell
III – Choir

Optional use of a solo reed is shown.

Note that manuals are coupled throughout as instructed at the start: II to III; II and III to I (though any solo reed should remain uncoupled).

Pedal is coupled to the manual indicated. Therefore if 'III' is indicated in the Pedal this includes coupling to II also since Swell and Choir are always joined.

Duration: 19 minutes

Vocal score on sale: ISMN 979-0-060-03027-7
Study score: ISMN 979-0-060-12488-4 / ISBN 978-0-85162-789-2
Performance materials available on hire

Organ reductions of other Finzi works for chorus & orchestra are available:

In terra pax (*arranged by Robert Gower*)
ISMN 979-0-060-13039-7 / ISBN 978-0-78454-120-0

Requiem da Camera (*arranged by Francis Jackson*)
ISMN 979-0-060-12891-2 / ISBN 978-1-78454-001-2

to Howard Ferguson

FOR ST CECILIA
Ceremonial Ode

EDMUND BLUNDEN

GERALD FINZI
Organ reduction by
ROBERT GOWER

★ III is uncoupled if the solo reed is on that manual

17
1
CHORUS SOPRANO
De-light - ful God - dess, in whose fash - ion - ings And fa - bles
Solo reed
I mf
mp
22
Truth still goes a - dorned;
tr
f
Solo reed
I
6
Solo reed
I
6

2
poco allargando
Re-source-ful Le-gend, taught by whom Time sings Of what had else been lost or scorned,
mp
mf
3
Maestoso ♩ = c92
Thine be our first de-vo-tion, while we throng On this re-turn-ing day to rev-er-ence
(I)
Solo reed
I
ff
mf cresc
f

allargando
4 a tempo
one, Thy fair - est, and her - self Time's sweet - est song Sing
Solo reed
largamente
5 Tempo I
out Ce - cil - ia's name, Sing out Ce - cil - ia's name, and earth is new be - gun.
Solo reed
Solo reed

ritardando
52
I
III
II
59
6
Meno mosso, solenne (♩ = c66)
CHORUS BASS
Changed is the age; mys - te - ri - ous, man's
TENOR SOLO
Changed is the age; mys - te - ri - ous, man's

★ From this point there is a gradual increase of tempo until the 2nd half of the bar at 9 allowing for the modifications at 8 (& and 2 bars hereafter) and at the first half of 9

8
poco allargando
senza rigore
Più mosso (♩ = c126)
e poco a poco più animando
of the fleet - ing year:
St Val - en - tine for love's ad - ven - ture beams,
SOP
St Val - en - tine for
I
II
love's ad - ven - ture beams,
St George is with us in war's i - ron gleams,
St
(I)
III

Più animato (♩ = c144)
St Duns tan whose red tongs clip Sa-tan's powers,
George is with us in war's i-ron gleams,
St Duns-tan whose red tongs
sfz
mf
fp
f
III p
III
9 tenuto Ancor più animato (♩ = c152)
St Swith - in with his for - ty days of
ALTO
clipt Sa-tan's powers,
St
I fff
reduce
mf
reduce
II
pp
III
p
tr
ff

101
showers,
And many - y an - oth - er
SOP
ALTO
Swith - in with his for - ty days St Swith - in with his for - ty days of showers,
And
III
I
II
mp
cresc
107
ritard
al
saint,
are fond - ly ours;
But
SOP
man - y an - oth - And man - y an - oth - er saint, are fond - ly ours;
Solo Oboe
Solo Clarinet
espr
(cresc)
f
p
II (8' only)

10
Molto meno mosso (♩ = c58)
♩ = ♪ of preceding (approx)
115
poco riten
Morendo
where in all the saint - ly com pa - ny is one be - loved be - yond me - lo - dious Ce - ci - ly?
me - lo - dious
pp
ppp
III
16'
★ ossia, bar 118–121
etc
120
ALTO
Ce - ci - ly? me - lo - dious Ce - ci - ly?
III
II
ppp

11 a tempo (♩ = c58)
125
TEN SOLO
How came you, la - dy of fierce mar-tyr-dom, How came you by your man - i - fold skill? You found the soul of mus - ic yet half
pp
8'
130
dumb, Deep - chained the ut-ter-ance that should fill The high carved roofs of life with tides of tone
allargando
12 Più movimento (♩ = c63)
e poco a poco animato
SOP
Then in a
III mp cresc
16'
III

137
poco tenuto
rap - ture con-scious of all these You threw the pal -ace o - pen; and the throne Blazed forth dom - in - ion of in -
f
ff
13
Animato (♩= c116)
143
-fin -i ties.
ff
mf
mp cresc poco a poco
mf
pesante

150
f
ff
14 L'istesso tempo
158
CHORUS SOP & ALTO
Straight, by this beau - ti - ful in - ven - tress giv - en Art's clue, a stu - dious an - gel a - lit from
p

165
15
TEN
ALTO
SOP
hea - ven And in good time a host of mor - tals too As Ce - ci - ly's dis - ci - ples saw the clue, Till through the
pp
173
ritard
West re - ech - o - ing gen - ius vied In mak - ing mu - sic where her clear notes
mf
8'

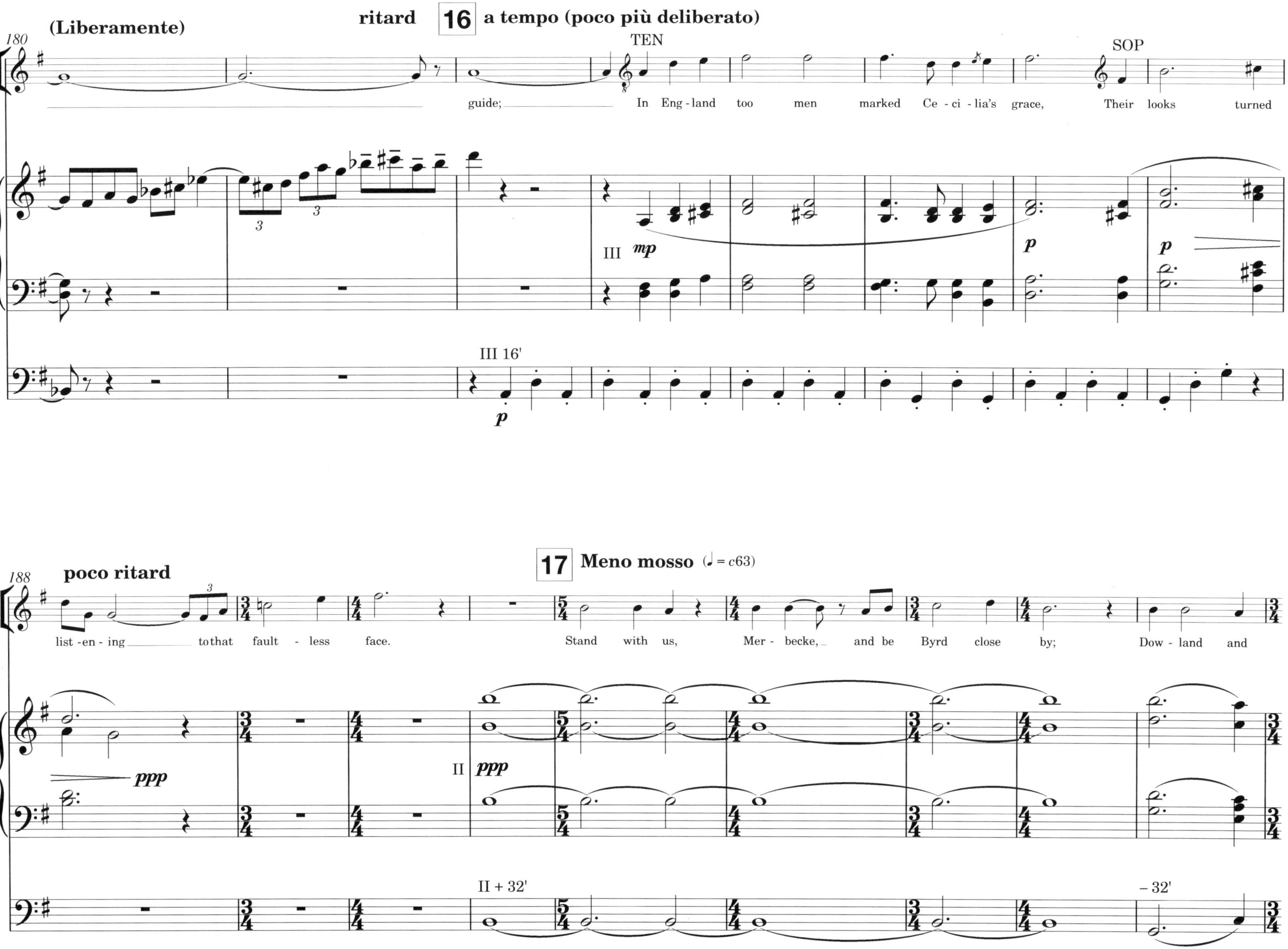
180
(Liberamente)
ritard
16
a tempo (poco più deliberato)
TEN
SOP
guide; In Eng - land too men marked Ce - ci - lia's grace, Their looks turned
III
mp
p
III 16'
188
poco ritard
17
Meno mosso (♩ = c63)
list - en - ing to that fault - less face. Stand with us, Mer - becke, and be Byrd close by; Dow - land and
ppp
II
II + 32'
– 32'

197
Pur - cell, lift the theme on high; Han - del is here, the friend and gen-er-ous guest, With mor - ning airs for her, and

207
18 Grazioso (𝅗𝅥 = c56)
chor - al zest.
III Solo Clarinet
pp mp
II
mp
II
II

215
TEN SOLO
How smil - ing - ly the saint a - mong her friends Sits, and with fin -
pp
222
- gers white and long A - wakes her own prae - lu - di - um, which trans - cends The

229
ad lib
u - nion of all oth - er song!
poco cresc
III
mp
mf
III
19
236
For ev - er these the first in arts re - main
And their o - rig - in - al blooms
p dolce
I
p
III

poco tenuto
on win - ter- less;
For ev - er
p
II
pp
II
20 a tempo
(Liberamente)
ritard
Ce - ci - ly's de - lights sus - tain
Song's
la - ter - com - ers, and her blue eyes
pp

21
ritard poco a poco
260
a tempo
SOP
bless.
her blue eyes bless.
pp
22
Allegro marcato (♩ = c126)
tenuto (♩ = c96)
accelerando
268
GP
Solo reed
f

276
a tempo (♩ = c126)
poco allargando
not coupled to solo reed
f
23 Maestoso ♩ = c72
282
TEN
Where - fore we bid you to the full con - cent Of St Ce - ci - lia's joy - ous ar - gu - ment,
ALTO
Where - fore we bid you to the full con cent Of
I
ffz
f sonoro
III
I
III
I

287
SOP
Where - fore we
St Ce - ci - lia's joy - ous ar - gu - ment, bid you to the full con - cent Of St Ce - ci - lia's joy - ous ar - gu - ment,
24
292
ALTO
And in her host we con - gre - gate each form
SOP
And in each host we con - gre - gate each form
Her Mu - sic takes when it would lull, or
f sostenuto

297
storm;
And ev-ery means that grew be-neath her hand To wing man's thought far past the ground he spanned.
ff
mf
cresc poco a poco
303
25
Ex-ult in mu-sic's strife and mu-sic's calm,
ff
ff
II
ppp
II

310
TEN
For all man's mar - tyr - dom the crown - ing psalm,
SOP
For all man's mar - tyr - dom the crown - ing psalm, The
III
dolce
p
I
315
ritard
gift of St Ce - cil - ia whose young voice Man doomed to death,
mp cresc poco a poco
mf
f

26
Deliberato ♩ = c56
SOP
TEN
and yet who could re - joice, and yet who could re - joice,
Sure of her dream that bears the world a - long
mp cresc
f
cresc
allargando
27 Grandioso
ALTO
dream that bears the world a - long,
Blest in the life, Blest in the
fff Solo reed

334
life,
Blest in the life,
Of u - ni - ver - sal song.
(Solo reed)
(fff)

340
tenuto a tempo
I
ff
Solo reed
Solo reed coupled to I
fffz
fffz

ISBN-13: 978-1-78454-121-7
DISTRIBUTED BY
HAL LEONARD
CORPORATION
48023601
8 88680 10374 3

ISBN 978-1-78454-121-7
9 781784 541217

BOOSEY & HAWKES

AN IMAGEM COMPANY

ISMN 979-0-060-13040-3
9 790060 130403